DEADLY DINOSAURS
MEGA-MEAT EATERS

igloobooks

CLOSE ENCOUNTER

This herd of Megalosaurus (MEG-UH-LOW-SAWR-US) are hunting their prey. Which of these images is the odd one out?

A

B

C

D

E

F

DIFFERENT DINO

Which close-up does not belong to this Albertosaurus (AL-BERT-OH-SAWR-US)?

A

B

C

D

E

Answers on page 16

ALLOSAURUS
(AL-OH-SAWR-US)

Period: Jurassic

203–135 million years ago

HEIGHT: 5m (17ft)
LENGTH: 12m (40ft)
WEIGHT: 1814kg (4000lbs)

FOOTPRINT PUZZLER

A Ceratosaurus (SIH-RAT-OH-SAWR-US) has trampled on this puzzle. Match each of the missing pieces to the correct gap in the picture.

A   **B**   **C**

D   **E**

ROAR DRAW

Copy the picture of this awesome Giganotosaurus (GIG-AH-NO-TOE-SAWR-US) into the grid below.

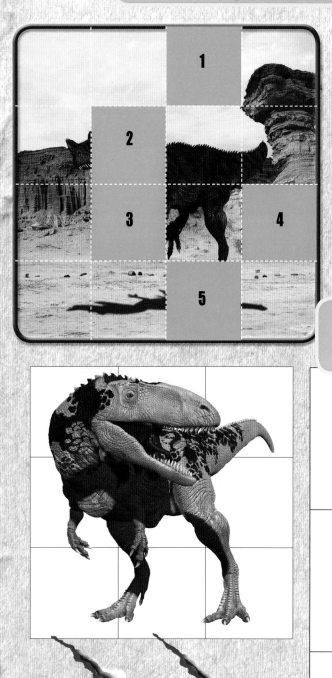

4

Answers on page 16

TYRANNOSAURUS LUNCH

This Tyrannosaurus (TIE-RAN-OH-SAWR-US) is making short work of his prey. Which detail does not appear in the scene?

A

B

C

D

E

F

DINO DRAW

Follow these step-by-step instructions to draw an amazing Megalosaurus (MEG-UH-LOW-SAWR-US).

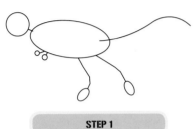

STEP 1

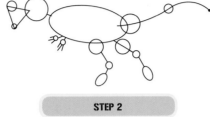

STEP 2

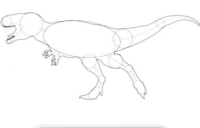

STEP 3

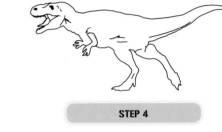

STEP 4

TYRANNOSAURUS
(TIE-RAN-OH-SAWR-US)

Period: Jurassic

203–135 million years ago

HEIGHT: 7m (27ft)

LENGTH: 15m (50ft)

WEIGHT: 6350kg (14,000lbs)

SPOT THE DIFFERENCE

This Tarbosaurus (TARB-UH-SAWR-US) is hunting
its prey. Circle the five differences between
the two pictures.

CARNOTAURUS TRAIL

This Carnotaurus (CAR-NO-TORE-US) is searching for food.
Which trail will lead it to the Iguanodon (IG-WAH-NA-DON)?

1

2

3

Answers on page 16

ALLOSAURUS

HEIGHT: 5m (17ft)

WEIGHT: 1814kg (3999lbs)

FEROCITY 9

The Allosaurus once inhabited what is now North America. Dozens of complete fossils have been found in quarries and other areas.

CERATOSAUR

HEIGHT: 2.5m (8ft)

WEIGHT: 1359kg (2996lbs)

FEROCITY 8

Unlike most similar predators, the Ceratosaur feasted on fish as well as other dinosaurs.

GIGANOTOSAURUS

HEIGHT: 7m (23ft)

WEIGHT: 8800kg (19,400lbs)

FEROCITY 4

Giganotosaurus hunted in packs, taking down huge dinosaurs in groups of three or four.

ALBERTOSAURUS

HEIGHT: 2.5m (8ft)

WEIGHT: 1724kg (3801lbs)

FEROCITY 6

This dinosaur is closely related to the T-Rex and preyed on small herbivores.

CARNOTAURUS

HEIGHT: 3m (10ft)

WEIGHT: 2087kg (4601lbs)

FEROCITY 6

This dinosaur was a huge creature but thanks to its very straight tail, it was able to reach high speeds.

IGUANODON

HEIGHT: 3m (10ft)

WEIGHT: 3175kg (7000lbs)

FEROCITY 3

Iguanodon fossils have been discovered all over the world - in Asia, Europe and North America.

Top Trumps

HOW TO PLAY:

1. Shuffle and divide the cards between two players. Each player must hold their cards face up in a pile in their hands, only looking at the top card.

2. Player one must read out an item from his/her top card (e.g. Ferocity 8). Player two must then read out the same item on his/her top card.

3. The player with the highest value wins and gets to take the other player's card.

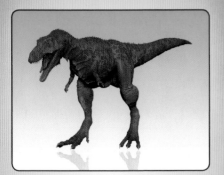

TARBOSAURUS

HEIGHT: 3.5m (11.5ft)

WEIGHT: 4536kg (10,000lbs)

FEROCITY ▮▮▮▮▮▮▮ **7**

Tarbosaurus was a deadly predator but often scavenged food from already dead dinosaurs.

SPINOSAURUS

HEIGHT: 5m (17ft)

WEIGHT: 4000kg (8816lbs)

FEROCITY ▮▮▮▮▮▮▮▮▮ **9**

The distinctive spine on the back of the Spinosaurus is supported by sharp needles of bone.

UTAHRAPTOR

HEIGHT: 2m (6ft)

WEIGHT: 500kg (1102lbs)

FEROCITY ▮▮▮▮▮▮▮▮▮ **9**

The Utahraptor had a claw on its hind legs that measured around a foot in length.

VELOCIRAPTOR

HEIGHT: 90cm (3ft)

WEIGHT: 15kg (33lbs)

FEROCITY ▮▮▮▮▮▮▮▮ **8**

The name 'velociraptor' comes from the Greek language and means speedy thief.

TYRANNOSAURUS

HEIGHT: 7m (23ft)

WEIGHT: 6350kg (14,000lbs)

FEROCITY ▮▮▮▮▮▮▮▮▮▮ **10**

The Tyrannosaurus Rex is one of the most popular dinosaurs. The name means 'Tyrant Lizard King'.

MEGALOSAURUS

HEIGHT: 3m (10ft)

WEIGHT: 2205 kg (4861lbs)

FEROCITY ▮▮▮▮▮▮▮ **7**

Megalosaurus was the first dinosaur ever to be named. Its name means 'Great Lizard'.

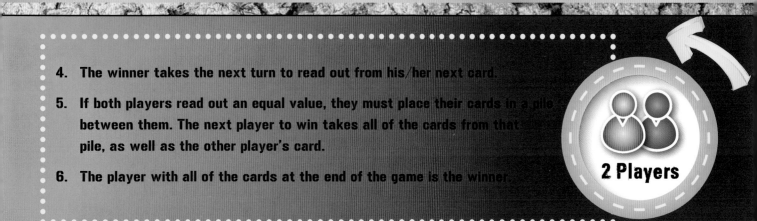

4. The winner takes the next turn to read out from his/her next card.

5. If both players read out an equal value, they must place their cards in a pile between them. The next player to win takes all of the cards from that pile, as well as the other player's card.

6. The player with all of the cards at the end of the game is the winner.

2 Players

SPINOSAURUS
SPY-NO-SAWR-US

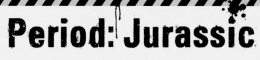

Period: Jurassic

203–135 million years ago

HEIGHT: 5m (17ft)

LENGTH: 15m (50ft)

WEIGHT: 6350kg (8816lbs)

ROUND-UP RAPTORS

These Utahraptor (YOO-TAH-RAP-TUH) are on the loose.
Round them up by drawing a line between each matching pair.

A

B

C

D

E

F

G

H

I

J

K

L

DINO DOTS

Join the dots on this fearsome Allosaurus (AL-OH-SAWR-US)
and then decorate it with your best pens.

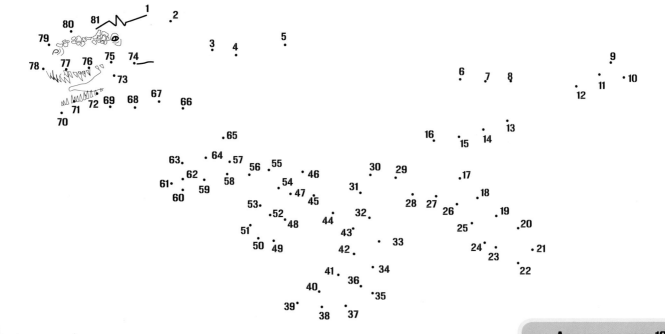

Answers on page 16

GIGANOTOSAURUS
(GIG-AH-NO-TOE-SAWR-US)

Period: Cretaceous

135–65 million years ago

HEIGHT: 7m (23ft)

LENGTH: 15m (46ft)

WEIGHT: 8800kg (19,400lbs)

MEGA MAZE

Help the Tyrannosaurus (TIE-RAN-OH-SAWR-US) get to its dinner by drawing a line through the maze.

START

FINISH

Answers on page 16

FIND AND COUNT

How many Velociraptor (VUH-LOSS-UH-RAP-TUH) can you find in this forest scene? Circle each one.

13

IN THE SHADOWS

Which of these shadows matches the frightening Allosaurus (AL-OH-SAWR-US) exactly?

A

B

C

D

MEAT-EATER MIX-UP

Put these four meat-eaters back together by drawing a line between two matching halves.

A

B

C

D

1

2

3

4

Answers on page 16

MEGALOSAURUS
(MEG-UH-LO-SAWR-US)

Period: Jurassic

203–135 million years ago

HEIGHT: 3m (10ft)

LENGTH: 9m (30ft)

WEIGHT: 1000kg (2205lbs)

ANSWER PAGE

Page 2
Close Encounter: C
Different Dino: F

Page 4
Footprint Puzzler:

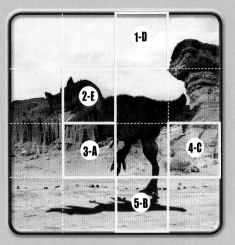

Page 5
Tyrannosaurus Lunch: C

Page 8
Spot the Difference:

Page 8
Carnotaurus Trail: Route 3

Page 10
Round-Up Raptors: A-L, B-J, C-F, D-H, E-K, G-I

Page 12
Mega Maze:

Page 13
Find and Count: 6 Velociraptors

Page 14
In the Shadows: Allosaurus C
Meat-Eater Mix-Up: A-3, B-4, C-2, D-1